It is a cold, dark evening in the city. It is snowing. A man with dark hair and very blue eyes is in a restaurant. He is sitting near the window. He is waiting. He is going to meet a woman here. He doesn't know her, but he knows her name.

A young woman is in a taxi. She is going to meet a man in a restaurant. She doesn't know him, but she knows his name.

The name of the woman in the taxi is Anna Brodsky. Anna works for a newspaper. She is a reporter. The name of the man in the restaurant is Tom Casey. He is a police detective.

Tom doesn't like reporters. Anna doesn't like detectives, but she wants to ask Tom some questions.

1

Anna goes into the restaurant. She sees a tall man with dark hair and blue eyes near the window. She walks to his table.

"Hello. Are you Tom Casey?" she asks.

"Yes, that's right. Are you the reporter? What do you want?"

"I want to interview you. I want to ask you some questions about your job."

"All right," Tom says. He doesn't smile.

Anna sits down. "Do you like your job?" she asks.

Tom looks at her for a moment.

"Sometimes I like it, and sometimes I don't like it."

"Why?"

"Most of the time I catch criminals *after* the crime. I'd like to stop more of them *before* the crime, and that's difficult."

In a dark street not far away, a young man is looking at cars. He has a gold ring on his middle finger, with the letter B on it. His name is Buck. He has long, red hair. He wants a car. A new car. Fast, and not too big.

Suddenly he sees a green BMW across the street. He smiles.

The soft snow is falling. Buck can't see any other people in the dark street. He looks up at the windows. They are dark, too. He runs across the street and stops beside the car door. He looks up again. Then he takes a ring full of keys from his pocket. He puts a key in the lock.

In the restaurant, Anna is asking Tom a question.
"How can you stop a criminal before the crime?"
Tom looks out of the window at the snow.
"Sometimes one crime is part of another crime," he says.
"How? I don't understand."
"It's like this. Someone takes a car and then robs a bank.
A good detective understands that the first crime is part of
the second crime."
"And what does a good detective do then?"
Tom smiles. "A good detective asks a lot of questions.
A good detective tries to think like the criminal. And
then a good detective waits."
Anna is thinking. This man isn't like other police
detectives. He's different. This is going to be a good
interview.

Nancy Green and her husband, Paul, are working late. They are in a small office above their shop. Paul is doing some calculations on a machine.

"Would you like some coffee, Paul?" Nancy asks.

"Yes. Good idea," he says.

She gets up and walks to the coffee machine beside the window.

In the dark street outside, Buck puts another key in the lock. Then another. His hands are cold but he works fast.

Nancy Green puts some water into the coffee machine. She opens the curtains and looks out of the window.

"The snow is very heavy now," she tells her husband.

She begins to turn away. But suddenly she stops, and looks out of the window again.

"There's someone in our car!" she says.

Paul Green runs out of the office.

"Paul!" Nancy shouts. "Don't go out there! Call the police!"

But Paul is in the dark street now.

"Stop! That's my car!" he shouts.

Buck starts the car. He turns the wheel and the car moves. He sees a man in the street but he doesn't stop. The car hits the man.

Buck is angry. "You were in my way!" he says. He drives very fast down the dark street. He comes to a big road. He wants to turn right, but the traffic is slow. On the left the traffic is moving fast. He turns left.

Paul Green is lying in the snow. Nancy runs to him.

"Are you all right?" she asks.

"My leg," he says, "My leg hurts."

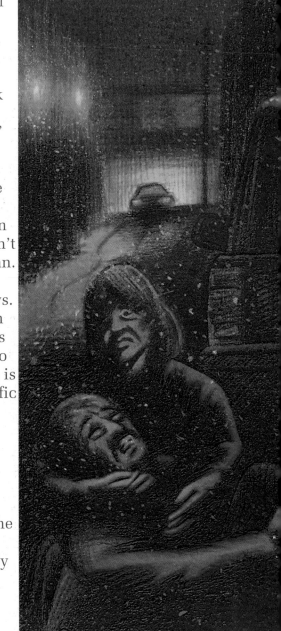

Tom takes a small telephone from his pocket. He speaks, and listens.

"I'm sorry, I can't stay," he tells Anna.

"Let me come with you," Anna says.

"A detective's job isn't always very nice," Tom tells her.

Anna smiles. "A reporter's job isn't always very nice either. Let's go."

They drive to a dark street not far away. Two men are putting Paul Green into an ambulance. A police officer is asking questions.

"He was young, with long hair," Nancy Green is saying.

"Is there anything else you can tell us?" Tom asks.

Nancy Green looks at the ambulance. She doesn't want all these questions.

Tom says nothing. He waits.

Then Nancy Green remembers. "The gas tank in the car. It's almost empty."

Buck sees a small red light inside the car. The red light means that the gas tank is almost empty. Then he sees some bright yellow lights near the bridge. He knows he can buy some gas there.

A boy in a yellow uniform runs out to the green BMW. "Fill the tank. Do it fast! I'm in a hurry!" Buck says.

The boy looks at the gold ring on Buck's middle finger. He can see a big B on it.

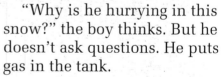

"Why is he hurrying in this snow?" the boy thinks. But he doesn't ask questions. He puts gas in the tank.

"It's full now," he tells Buck.

Buck pays him and drives away. The boy in the yellow uniform watches him.

The ambulance goes, and the street is dark again. Tom
and Anna are sitting in Tom's car.

"He drove down this street," Anna says. "The woman
saw him."

"But where did he go then?" Tom asks.

They drive down the dark street. They come to the big
road. The traffic is moving in both directions.

"I think he turned left here," Anna says.

"Why?"

"The traffic on the left is going fast. And he was in a
hurry."

"OK," Tom says. He is thinking. This woman isn't like
other reporters. She's different.

They turn left and drive to the bridge. Then Tom sees
the gas station.

The snow is still falling.

Buck drives across the bridge. Two police officers in a car see him.

"Why is he driving so fast in this snow?" says the first officer.

Buck turns right, into a long, dark street. There is an old factory at the end of the street. The big factory doors open, and then they close again, behind Buck and the car.

"Call Casey," says the second police officer.

"Yeah. A green BMW stopped here. I filled the tank," a boy in a yellow uniform tells Tom.

"What about the driver?"

"He was young."

"Is that all you remember?"

"Yeah."

Tom waits a moment. Then the boy says: "Oh, and he had long, red hair... and a gold ring with the letter B on it."

"Long red hair and a gold ring with the letter B on it," says Tom. "I remember him. Buck Jackson. He's a thief. A car thief."

"What does he do with the cars?" Anna asks.

"Sometimes he works with other criminals. Sometimes they want a fast car and a driver."

"To rob a bank, or something?"

Tom is thinking fast. The Moran brothers are here in the city. They rob banks. Two police officers are watching them now.

"That's right," he says.

Buck is inside the factory. He is talking to a big man with a beard.

"It's small, Mr Moran. And it's fast," Buck tells him.

The big man looks at the car for a long time.

"All right. Change the licence plate. You're driving it tomorrow morning."

It isn't snowing now, but the city streets are still dark.
Anna is in Tom's office at the police station.

"Two officers saw Buck Jackson," Tom tells her. "He's in
an old factory, with the Moran brothers. So is the car. I
think they're going to rob a bank."

"What are you going to do now?" she asks.

"What do you think I'm going to do?"

"I think you're going to wait."

Tom smiles. "Wait with me. I don't think we're going to
wait very long," he tells Anna.

At 6.15 in the morning, Tom's telephone rings.

"Casey. Fourth District," Tom says and listens.
Then he looks at Anna.

"They're coming out of the factory now, in a green BMW.
A new licence plate, but the same car."

Tom looks at his watch. "The banks aren't open now," he says.

Anna thinks for a moment.

"No, but it's Tuesday. The City Bank, on Park and 14th Street, gets money early every Tuesday morning. They bring the money in a Central Security Company truck."

"How do you know?"

"I'm a reporter. It's my job to know things like that."

Tom looks at a map of the city.

"Trucks come into the city on Lincoln Boulevard. Buck and his friends are going to stop this one on Lincoln and 13th," he says.

"How do you know?" she asks.

"I'm a detective. It's my job to know things like that."

Tom telephones the Central Security Company. The truck is coming now. It is carrying a million dollars.

It is 6.45. Anna and Tom are waiting in a car at Lincoln Boulevard and 13th Street. They are very near the City Freeway.

"That's the only fast road out of the city," Tom says.

A big grey truck is coming towards them. It has CSC on it in big letters.

"There's the security truck," Anna says.

Suddenly, a green BMW drives very fast across Lincoln Boulevard, in front of the security truck. The truck and the car both stop. Three men jump out of the BMW – Buck and the two Moran brothers. One of them has a gun. He shoots through the door of the security truck.

The officers of Fourth District are waiting for this.

"Stop there! Police!"

The three men stop and look. The police are all around them. They can't run now. They put their hands up. The police take Buck and his two friends away.

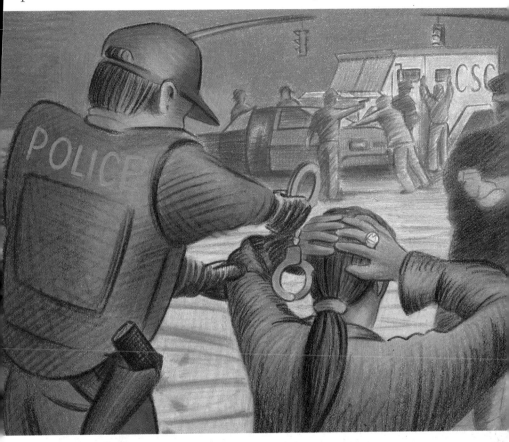

Tom takes Anna to her office at the newspaper. He stops the car outside. The streets aren't dark now. The sun is shining on the white snow.

"What about your interview?" he asks.

Anna opens the car door. She hasn't got her interview, but she has a good story for her newspaper. She smiles.

"Can I interview you again?" she asks.

"Yes. What about this evening? For dinner."

ACTIVITIES

Before you read

1 Look at the picture on the front cover. What is happening?

2 What type of story do you think this is?
a) adventure b) crime c) travel

3 Check these words in your dictionary, then use them to complete the sentences: *snow   thief   traffic   empty*
a) The box was ....., there was nothing in it.
b) A ..... is taking our radio. Stop him!
c) Ice and ..... are cold.
d) There is always a lot of ..... in the city.

After you read

4 What do these people do for a living?
Tom Casey   Anna Brodsky   the Moran brothers

5 Why is Anna meeting Tom?

6 Complete these sentences with *before* or *after*.
a) Buck changes the licence plate ..... he buys gas.
b) Nancy Green runs outside ..... her husband.
c) Tom catches the criminals ..... the second crime.

7 What do these people remember, and why is it important?
Nancy Green   the boy at the gas station

8 How does Anna help Tom?

9 What is the CSC truck carrying?

10 Design a police *Wanted* poster for Buck Jackson. Say what he looks like, and why the police want to find him.

Writing

11 What do you think the police officer and Tom Casey say to each other on the police radio (page 10)? Write out their conversation.

12 What happens at Lincoln Boulevard and 13th Street early on Tuesday morning? Write a short report for the newspaper.